1

ALSO BY CHARLEY PARKER:

ARGON ZARK!

DINOSAUR CARTOONS

BY CHARLEY PARKER

FOR JOHANNA

SPECIAL THANKS TO GARDNER DOZOIS AND BOB WALTERS

DINOSAUR CARTOONS BY CHARLEY PARKER

A DINOSAURCARTOONS.COM BOOK
PUBLISHED BY ARCLIGHT PUBLISHING, PO BOX 437, WALLINGFORD, PA 19086
PRINTED IN THE UNITED STATES OF AMERICA
ISBN 0-9660532-1-4

SEVERAL OF THE CARTOONS IN THIS EDITION WERE ORIGINALLY
PUBLISHED IN ASIMOV'S SCIENCE FICTION.

DINOSAUR CARTOONS
BY CHARLEY PARKER

A DinosaurCartoons.com™ book

I FORGET. ARE WE BRONTOSAURS, APATOSAURS, OR WHAT?

"WELL, I HOPE YOU'RE ALL READY FOR YOUR FINAL EXAM."

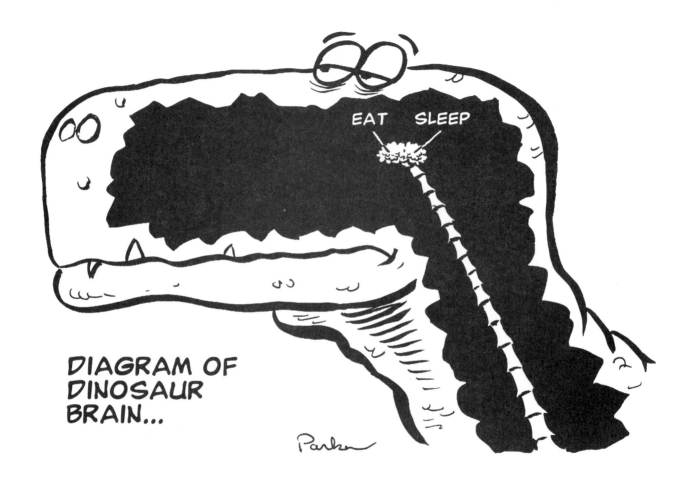

EAT   SLEEP

DIAGRAM OF
DINOSAUR
BRAIN...

STANDARD MODEL

WITH ACCESSORIES

13

THE LONE RANGER AND BRONTO

14

TARZAN OF THE JURASSIC

16

SWISS ARMY
DINOSAUR

DINOSORE

BOOKS ON DINOSAURS

"MISS JENKINS, BRING ME A BLACK COFFEE AND TWO DAZED MAMMALS"

22

Parker

23

GODZILLA VS. RAMBO, ROCKY, PREDATOR, TERMINATOR ALIENS, CHUCK NORRIS, CHARLES BRONSON, CLINT EASTWOOD, STEVEN SEGAL, AND JEAN CLAUDE VAN DAMME.

"MARJORIE! I'VE TOLD YOU BEFORE! DON'T FEED HIM TABLE SCRAPS!"

29

30

"DON'T PLAY WITH THAT! YOU'LL POKE YOUR EYE OUT!"

WOOLY
MAMMOTH

SPANDEX ACRYLIC
MAMMOTH

33

"GREAT! NOW *WE* HAVE TO GET A *STEGOSAURUS!*"

"DON'T EVER EVOLVE, BABY, I LOVE YOU JUST THE WAY YOU ARE."

37

"I FEEL PTERRIBLE."

40

"TRY TO AVOID EYE CONTACT"

41

"THAT'S IT! STARTING TOMORROW, NOTHING BUT DECAF."

"NOPE. IT'S STILL A GRANNY. TRY AGAIN."

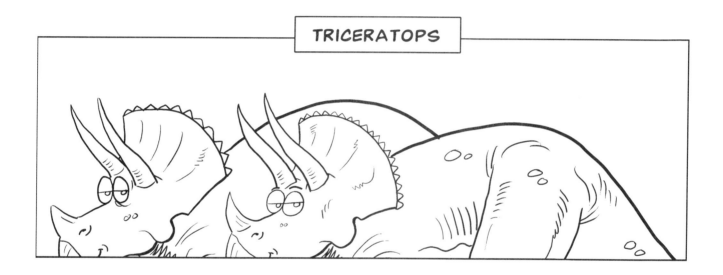

TRICERATOPS

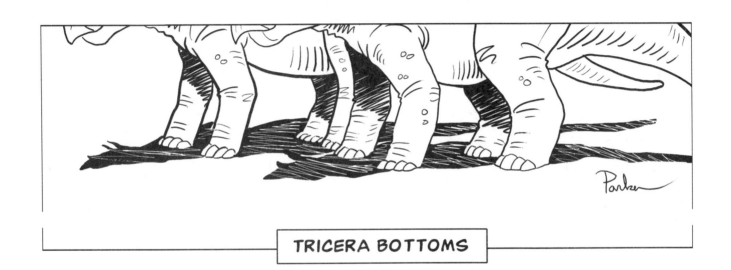

TRICERA BOTTOMS

46

"TRÈS CHIC! AND *WAY* AHEAD OF ITS TIME!"

ALLOSAURUS IN WONDERLAND

51

"SORRY, THEY ALL HAVE TO COME OUT."

YOU **CAUGHT** IT, **YOU** CLEAN IT!

"LET'S FACE IT, YOU DON'T HAVE ANY IDEA WHAT THEY'RE FOR, EITHER."

SINCE THE DAWN OF TIME

57

"HEY! THERE'S NO "I" IN STYRACOSAURUS!"

"I'M NOT BACKING UP! *YOU* BACK UP!"

60

"BRILLIANT DISGUISE, HOLMES!"

"FIVE MINUTES ON *NOVA* AND HE'S MR. HOLLYWOOD!"

"HAVE YOU CONSIDERED SEEING A CHIROPRACTOR?"

...CONTINUED HOT AND EXTREMELY HUMID TODAY, HIGHS NEAR 110,
WITH THUNDERSTORMS AND HEAVY DOWNPOURS LIKELY THROUGHOUT
THE DAY AND PERHAPS A SPRINKLING OF VOLCANIC ASH.
LOOKS LIKE ANOTHER NICE ONE, SO GET OUT AND ENJOY!

68

"WE HAVE TO STOP MEETING LIKE THIS."

"UH, THANKS,.... I'LL TAKE THE NEXT CAR."

"OH HOW NICE... YOU BROUGHT DESSERT!"

DINOSAUR FURNITURE

"GLORIA! CAN'T YOU SEE HE DOESN'T LOVE YOU FOR YOUR *MIND?!*"

74

76

"..AND I CAN'T *BELIEVE* SHE SAID THAT! IF IT WERE
UP TO *ME,* I'D... *HEY!* ARE YOU EVEN *LISTENING* TO ME?"

DINERSAUR

81

"WOW! A PTERODACTYL'S-EYE VIEW!"

83

"WELL, I CERTAINLY HOPE YOU'VE HAD HIM NEUTERED!"

84

"OH, I DON'T KNOW... WHAT DO YOU WANT TO BE WHEN **YOU** EVOLVE?"

"EDWARD! DON'T BE SO RUDE!
OUR GUEST HASN'T STARTED YET."

"LOVED HIM, HATED HER."

GIDDYUP!

"YES, HE'S CUTE, BUT I WOULDN'T PUT YOUR FINGER IN THERE."

93

"*LOVE* THE NOSE JOB."

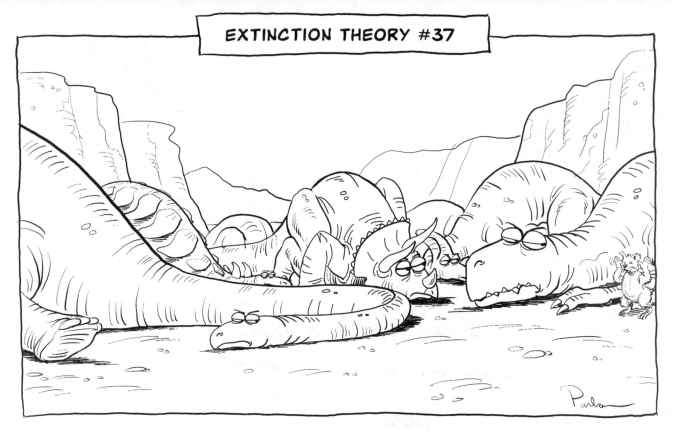

THE DINOSAURS WERE DOING GREAT UNTIL ONE DAY, GOD TURNED UP THE GRAVITY.

MONA LISAUR

Parker

"OH GREAT, NOW HE'S HIRED AN EFFICIENCY EXPERT."

"FOR YOUR INFORMATION, THE EARTH MOVED FOR THE REST OF US, TOO."

HEY! WHO TOOK MY RUBBER PLESIOSAUR?

"I DON'T KNOW,.... I JUST DON'T THINK IT'S *DANK* ENOUGH."

102

EXTINCTION THEORY #485

THE DINOSAURS AREN'T REALLY EXTINCT, THEY'RE
LIVING IN ARGENTINA UNDER ASSUMED NAMES.

103

"...BUT YOU KNEW I WAS COLD-BLOODED WHEN YOU MARRIED ME."

104

"..AND THERE'S NOT A THING YOU CAN DO ABOUT IT!"

"UH, RALPH?... I THINK YOU'LL WANT TO TAKE A LOOK AT THIS..."

"OH, GIVE ME A HOME, WHERE THE *STRUTHIOMIMUS* ROAM,
AND THE *HYPSILOPHODONS* AND THE *PACHYCEPHALOSAURS* PLAAAAAY..."

"GESUNDHEIT."

111

ABOUT THE AUTHOR

CHARLEY PARKER IS A CARTOONIST, COMIC BOOK CREATOR AND DIGITAL ARTIST LIVING IN THE PHILADELPHIA AREA. HE WAS BORN IN THE LATE CRETACEOUS AND SEEMS TO HAVE DEVELOPED SPECIALIZED APPENDAGES FOR GRIPPING PENS AND STYLI FOR DIGITAL DRAWING TABLETS. THE FOSSIL RECORD LEAVES FEW CLUES AS TO HIS OTHER CHARACTERISTICS.

HE IS ALSO THE CREATOR OF *ARGON ZARK!* THE ORIGINAL INTERACTIVE ONLINE COMIC AT *WWW.ZARK.COM.*